50 C...
GERM...
AND 2...

by

R.N. SOAR

BERNARD BABANI (publishing) LTD
THE GRAMPIANS
SHEPHERDS BUSH ROAD
LONDON W6 7NF
ENGLAND

Please Note

Although every care has been taken with the production of this book to ensure that any projects, designs, modifications and/or programs etc. contained herewith, operate in a correct and safe manner and also that any components specified are normally available in Great Britain, the Publishers do not accept responsibility in any way for the failure, including fault in design, of any project, design, modification or program to work correctly or to cause damage to any other equipment that it may be connected to or used in conjunction with, or in respect of any other damage or injury that may be so caused, nor do the Publishers accept responsibility in any way for the failure to obtain specified components.

Notice is also given that if equipment that is still under warranty is modified in any way or used or connected with home-built equipment then that warranty may be void.

Printed and Bound in Great Britain by Cox & Wyman Ltd, Reading

CONTENTS

INTRODUCTION

This book contains circuits using germanium, silicon and zener diodes.

For circuits using OA91 germanium diodes, types OA81, OA95, OA70, OA85 or AA118 can be used as alternatives, in practice almost any good quality germanium signal diodes will work in these circuits.

An equivalent for the OA79 is the 1N60 and for the OA90 is the AA116.

For the circuits using 1N914 diodes, 1N4148 or BA127 can be used. These diodes are silicon signal high speed types, silicon rectifiers are NOT suitable.

For circuits in which silicon rectifiers types 1N4001, 1N4002 or 1N4007 are specified, an equivalent for the 1N4007 is the BY127.

Also the ratings are:

1N4001	1 Amp	50 piv
1N4002	1 Amp	100 piv
1N4007	1 Amp	1000 piv

A silicon rectifier of the same rating can be used without affecting circuit operation. It is always possible to use a rectifier of *higher* specification in place of one specified, e.g. a 1N4002 instead of a 1N4001 or a 1N4007 instead of a 1N4002.

For zener diodes a voltage and wattage is specified, e.g. 9.1V 400mW. It is always possible, apart from size considerations, to use a zener of higher wattage than specified, e.g. a 1W zener instead of a 400mW.

The normal voltage range for 400mW zeners is from 2.7V to 33V. The entire series is:

2.7, 3.0, 3.3, 3.6, 3.9, 4.3, 4.7, 5.1, 5.6, 6.2, 6.8, 7.5, 8.2, 10, 11, 12, 13, 15, 16, 18, 20, 22, 24, 27, 30, 33.

5

Zener diodes of higher wattages are available in voltages up to 200V. The highest wattage rating available normally is 10W or 20W stud mounting, cathode is stud. Special 100W 12V zeners are sometimes used as motorcycle voltage regulators. These must be mounted on a suitable heat sink.

Special 33V zener equivalent two terminal integrated circuit voltage stabilisers such as the TAA550 are now used to provide a voltage reference for varicap diode tuners in television sets.

Circuit 45 uses an unusual type of diode, the tunnel diode as a two-terminal AF oscillator. This circuit may appeal to the experimenter.

CIRCUIT ONE

MEDIUM WAVE TUNER FOR USE WITH AUDIO AMPLIFIER

This is a simple diode demodulator tuner for use with an audio amplifier. With a few feet of aerial wire it will give good reception of two or three local MW transmissions. The quality of reproduction is good, the only real disadvantage of such a simple tuner as this is the lack of selectivity, this may be a problem after dark when foreign stations come within range.

If only one MW station is required the tuning capacitor can be a 500pF trimmer, reducing the cost, as 500pF variable capacitors are quite expensive.

The coil former can be a cardboard tube or short piece of wooden dowel about 1½" diameter.

The coil for MW use is 70 turns of 26 or 28 swg enamelled wire tapped at 35 turns.

If you wish to experiment with short wave reception try a coil of 20 turns tapped at 10 turns.

The MW tuner may find further use as a transistor radio booster.

6

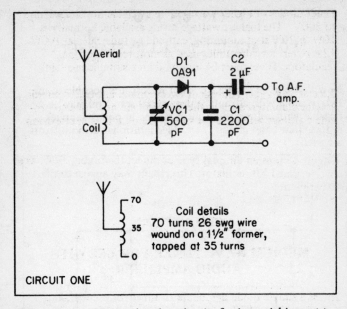

Coil details
70 turns 26 swg wire
wound on a 1½" former,
tapped at 35 turns

CIRCUIT ONE

If a transistor radio is placed so that its ferrite aerial is next to
the MW tuner tuning coil and the transistor radio is tuned to
a weak transmission, slowly tune the MW tuner to the same
frequency there will be a great improvement in the transistor
radio reception due to signal being coupled via the MW tuner.
Using this method distant low power MW transmissions can be
received.

Components List

VC1	500pf variable capacitor
C1	2200pF
C2	2µF 16V
D1	OA91 germanium diode.

CIRCUIT TWO

VOLTAGE DOUBLER CRYSTAL SET

Now that crystal diodes are lower in cost it is possible to use
two or more with advantage in a crystal set. You may be
familiar with voltage multipliers as used in power supplies
in this circuit and circuit (3) voltage multiplier demodulators
are used.

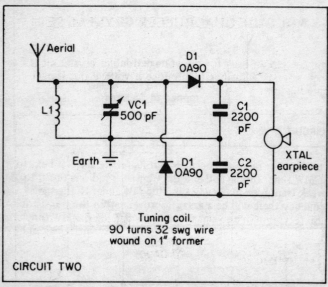

Tuning coil.
90 turns 32 swg wire
wound on 1" former

CIRCUIT TWO

The diodes D1 and D2 charge up capacitors C1 and C2 and the
earphone is operated by the sum voltage across C1 and C2. It
is very important that the earphone employed is a CRYSTAL
earphone, the crystal earphone utilises a piezoelectric crystal,
hence the name, to cause movements in the earphone
diaphram and is a *voltage* operated device, the ordinary type
of earpiece as usually supplied with transistor radios is not
suitable. The crystal set coil is 90 turns of 32 swg enamelled
wire wound on a 1 inch cardboard tube.

The crystal set should be used with a good aerial and an
earth.

Components List

VC1	500pF variable capacitor
D1, D2	OA90 germanium diode
C1, C2	0.0022μF (2200pF) capacitor

CIRCUIT THREE

VOLTAGE QUADRUPLER CRYSTAL SET

Here the circuit used for the voltage doubler crystal set is taken one stage further to produce a voltage quadrupler demodulator.

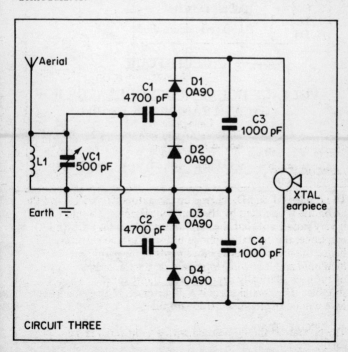

CIRCUIT THREE

The coil used is the same as for the voltage doubler set. As before it is essential that a crystal earpiece be used with this circuit, together with a good aerial and earth. The crystal diodes used must be full specification first grade diodes, some surplus type diodes work as rectifiers but make very poor detectors. Most complaints about non-functional crystal sets are due either to trying to use the crystal set with an inadequate aerial or a substandard diode in the circuit.

Note that germanium diodes should be soldered with care as overheating can damage the diode.

Try the set late at night, when it is quiet and traffic noise is low.

Components List

L1	as circuit (2)
VC1	500pF variable capacitor
C1, C2,	4700pF capacitor
C3, C4	1000pF capacitor
D1, D2, D3, D4	} OA90 germanium diode

CIRCUIT FOUR

VOLTAGE DOUBLER DEMODULATOR FOR USE IN TRANSISTOR RADIO

Here the voltage doubler principle is used to form a voltage doubler demodulator for use in a transistor radio superhet circuit.

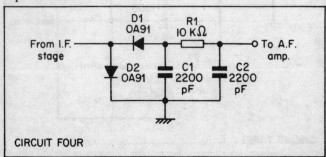

CIRCUIT FOUR

C1, C2 and R1 form a RF filter to remove any I.F. present in the output from the demodulator diodes.

Components List

D1, D2	OA91 germanium diode
C1, C2	2200pF capacitor
R1	10kΩ ¼W resistor.

CIRCUIT FIVE

SHORT RANGE 27MHz MODEL CONTROL RECEIVER

This is a short range receiver for use on the 27MHz radio control band.

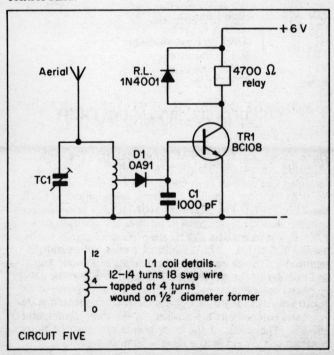

CIRCUIT FIVE

11

In effect it is a 27MHz crystal set. The transistor is a
D.C. amp to improve the sensitivity of the relay. The
1N4001 rectifier protects the transistor from damage due
to the back emf generated by the relay coil in operation.

The coil is 12 to 14 turns of 18 swg would on a ½" coil
former the coil is tuned to resonance by a 30pF trimmer.
It may also be necessary to compress or expand the coil in
order to bring the circuit in tune.

The circuit only has a short range due to the simplicity of the
circuit. However it provides a low cost method of converting
model boats to radio control. The only additional device
required for a model boat is an actuator for the steering.

Components List

TC1	30pF trimmer
C1	1000pF capacitor
D1	OA91 germanium diode
TR1	BC108 transistor
R1	1N4001 rectifier
Relay	4700Ω type

CIRCUITS SIX, SEVEN AND EIGHT

These circuit are typical FM demodulators. The coils
indicated are usually bought ready built complete in a
screening can as such coils are critical and difficult for the
home constructor to build. The latest development in FM is
the ZENITH/GE FM STEREO MULTIPLEX transmission
system. The multiplex system involves the addition of a
19KHz pilot tone and a 38KHz suppressed subcarrier to the
normal FM signal. This additional stereo information is
removed by the de-emphasis components in a mono tuner,
and in order to convert a mono FM tuner to stereo the de-
emphasis components must be removed. In order to assist
constructors in identifying de-emphasis components the de-
emphasis components are marked on the three demoulator
circuits. The values of the components vary but the time
constant will always be the same — 50 microseconds.

12

Each circuit uses a pair of OA91 diodes. These should be a matched pair for the best performance of the demodulator. When repairing an FM demodulator circuit, if one diode is faulty, replace both with a matched pair.

In some countries, e.g. the USA a de-emphasis of 75 microseconds is used.

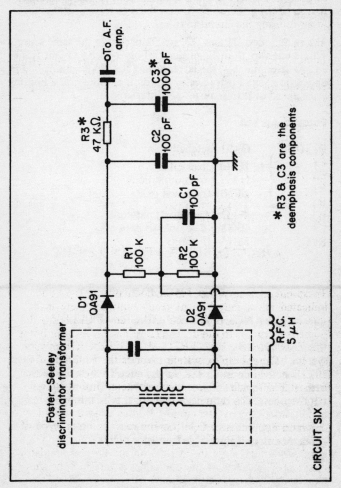

CIRCUIT SIX

CIRCUIT SIX

FOSTER-SEELEY DISCRIMINATOR

This is a balanced circuit, the two resistors R1 and R2 must
be closely matched in value. Two per cent tolerance resistors
should be used.

The two diodes, D1 and D2, are connected in the same sense.
This is one way of distinguishing a Foster-Seeley circuit from
a ratio discriminator, the latter having the diodes connected in
opposition. The Foster-Seeley discriminator requires a limiting
stage ahead of it to remove AM interference.

Components List

D1, D2	OA91 matched pair
C1	} 100pF silver mica
C2	
R1	} 100kΩ 2% metal oxide
R2	
R3	47kΩ de-emphasis network
C3	1000pF de-emphasis network
RFC	5μH VHF choke

CIRCUIT SEVEN

BALANCED RATIO DISCRIMINATOR
10.7 MHz FM

This is a balanced ratio discriminator circuit. Note that diodes
are connected in opposition. As the circuit is balanced about
earth it can provide an error voltage, when off tune, for an
A.F.C. circuit. The ratio discriminator is self-limiting.

The ratio discriminator is by far the most common type of
FM demodulator in portable transistor radios.

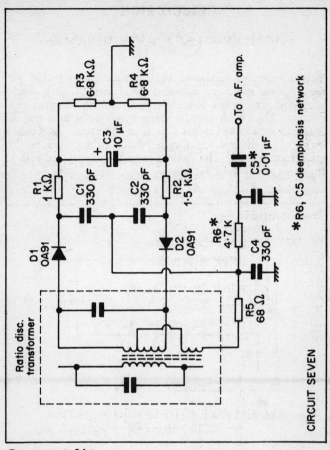

CIRCUIT SEVEN

Components List

	C1	330pF
	C2	330pF
D1, D2	OA91 matched pair	C3	10μF 16V
R1	1KΩ	C4	330pF
R2	1.5KΩ	
R3	6.8KΩ } 5% ¼W	
R4	6.8KΩ	
R5	68Ω	
R6	4.7k } de-emphasis network	
C5	0.01μF	

15

CIRCUIT EIGHT

UNBALANCED RATIO DISCRIMINATOR
10.7 MHz FM

This is a simpler version of the ratio discriminator FM demodulator and is not balanced about earth. This is the economy version FM demodulator as used in inexpensive circuits. The circuit uses far fewer components than the balanced version and is less critical in operation. As would be expected the audio quality is inferior to the balanced ratio discriminator. The diodes need not be a matched pair to obtain satisfactory operation.

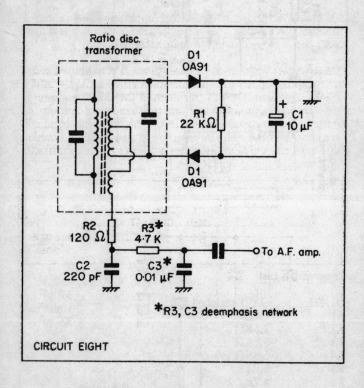

CIRCUIT EIGHT

Components List

R1	22KΩ
R2	120Ω
C1	10μF 16V
C2	220pF
R3	4.7k
C3	0.01μF
D1, D2	OA91 germanium diodes

R3 and C3: de-emphasis network

CIRCUIT NINE

SSB PRODUCT DETECTOR

On the MW band a normal AM (Amplitude Modulation) transmission consists of a carrier frequency plus two sets of sidebands which contain the audio information.

On the Short Wave Amateur bands space is very limited and a "cut to the bone" AM transmission method is used — SSB (Single Side Band). With this method the carrier and one side band are eliminated and one side band only is transmitted. Nothing vital has been lost — the single side band still contains the same audio information as an equivalent double side band transmission. However a different technique has to be employed in demodulation.

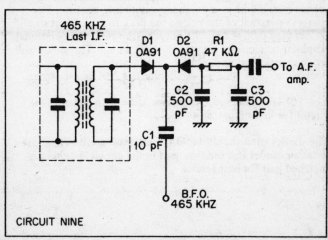

CIRCUIT NINE

In order to demodulate a SSB signal a carrier frequency is needed. This is provided by a BFO (Beat Frequency Oscillator) working at the IF of the superhet, 465KHz in circuit nine. When a 465KHz carrier is injected into the product detector the audio information is recovered. The frequency of the BFO is variable, about 465KHz, so that it can be adjusted to the exact frequency. When the BFO is off frequency this produces distortion of the audio.

Components List

D1, D2	OA91 germanium diode	
C1	10pF	
R1	47KΩ	
C1	500pF	} IF filter
C2	500pF	

CIRCUIT TEN

AUDIO FREQUENCY DOUBLER

This circuit employs the low level characteristics of a germanium diode in a frequency doubling circuit. For correct operation of the circuit the peak to peak input should be less than 0.05 volts. The output from the 741 operational amplifier is twice the frequency of the input. The circuit will work at 19KHz and could be used in a stereo decoder to double the pilot tone to regenerate the 38KHz subcarrier.

The 10KHz preset potentiometer is used to balance the circuit for minimum distortion.

The diodes used should be OA79 or equivalent. These are detector diodes and the two used in the circuit should be a matched pair for best results.

18

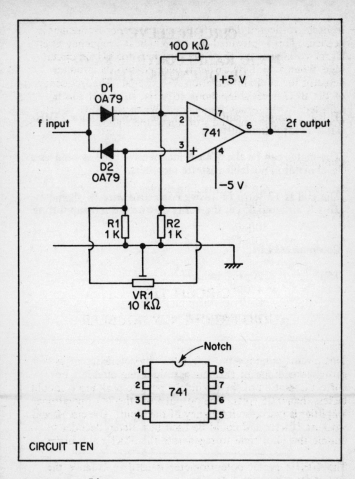

CIRCUIT TEN

Components List

D1, D2	OA79 matched pair
R1	1KΩ } 5% ¼W
R2	1KΩ
VR1	10KΩ preset potentiometer
R3	100KΩ
IC	741 8 pin D.I.L. operational amplifier

19

CIRCUIT ELEVEN

27MHz RADIO CONTROL BAND FREQUENCY METER

This is a simple circuit to check the output from a 27MHz radio control transmitter.

The meter can be the 500µA inexpensive type as used as a level meter in portable cassette recorders.

The coil is 12 turns of 18swg enamelled wire ½" diameter. This is air wound, i.e. the turns of wire are self-supporting.

Components List

TC1	30pF Trimmer
C1	470pF
D1	OA91 germanium diode
Meter	500 microamp

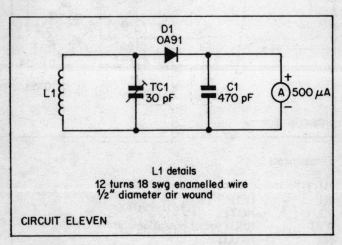

L1 details
12 turns 18 swg enamelled wire
½" diameter air wound

CIRCUIT ELEVEN

CIRCUIT TWELVE

AC/DC VOLTMETER

This is a simple voltmeter to measure 10 or 100 volts AC or DC. The meter used is a 500 microamp type which should be calibrated 0–10.

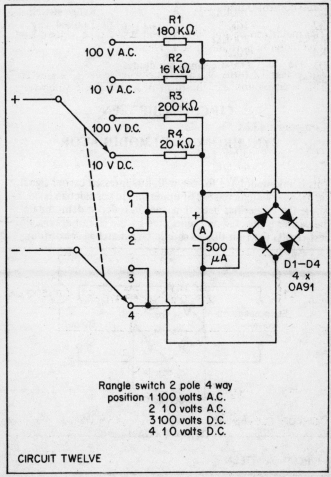

Rangle switch 2 pole 4 way
position 1 100 volts A.C.
2 1 0 volts A.C.
3 100 volts D.C.
4 1 0 volts D.C.

CIRCUIT TWELVE

The diodes D1–D4 form a bridge rectifier for use on the AC ranges. The values of the resistors R2–R4 are unusual but are available in the 5% E24 series. The switch is a 2 pole 4 way rotary type.

Components List

R1	180KΩ	⎫	Range switch
R2	16KΩ	⎬ 5% ¼W	2 pole 4 way
R3	200KΩ		
R4	20KΩ	⎭	
D1–D4	OA91 germanium diodes		
Meter	500 microamp		

CIRCUIT THIRTEEN

SYNCHRONOUS DEMODULATOR

This is a demodulator for use with a suppressed carrier signal, i.e. a signal which consists of upper and lower sidebands where the carrier has been removed. In order to demodulate the carrier is injected and reinserted by the circuit action. For best results the four diodes should be a matched set of four.

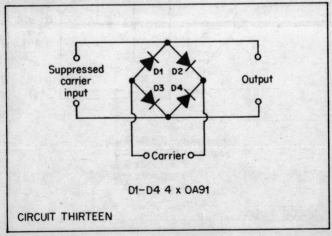

CIRCUIT THIRTEEN

This circuit can be used in a stereo decoder, the stereo information is carried by a 38KHz suppressed subcarrier. The input at the carrier terminals should be the regenerated 38KHz obtained by doubling the 19KHz pilot tone.

CIRCUIT FOURTEEN

LOW POWER 9V SUPPLY

This is a very low power 9V supply suitable for operating a preamplifier etc. with a current consumption of ·5mA or less. The circuit is powered from a 6.3V AC heater winding. The supply consists of a voltage doubler followed by a 9.1V stabiliser. The very low current means that OA91 germanium diodes can be used as rectifiers.

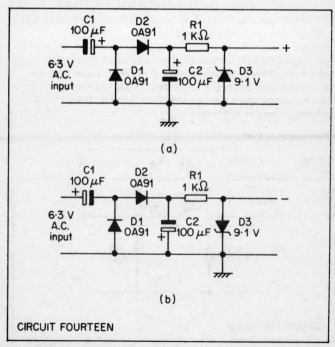

(a)

(b)

CIRCUIT FOURTEEN

Circuit (a) is a negative earth supply, circuit (b) has the polarities reversed to provide a positive earth supply.

Components List

D1, D2	OA91 germanium diodes
C1, C2	100µF 25V electrolytic capacitor
R1	1K Ω¼W
D3	9.1V 400mW zener diode

CIRCUIT FIFTEEN

AUDIO LIMITER

This is a simple limiter for use in radio circuits, the two diodes are connected in inverse parallel, each diode conducts at about 0.7 volts and the input is limited to this level.

The circuit can also be used at the aerial input to prevent overloading by strong nearby transmitters.

The diodes used in circuits 15, 16 are silicon signal diodes type 1N914 or 1N4148, these are high speed diodes, the normal silicon rectifiers are not suitable as they are only designed for low frequency operation, such as the 50 or 60, 100 or 120 Hz frequencies in mains circuits.

Components List

D1, D2   1N914 or 1N4148 silicon signal diodes

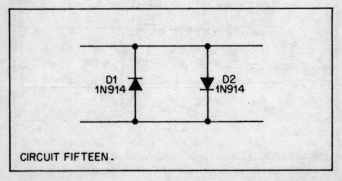

CIRCUIT FIFTEEN.

CIRCUIT SIXTEEN

AUDIO LIMITER FOR S.W. RADIO

This is an audio limiter for use in a S.W. radio to prevent over-loading on strong transmissions and produces a better balance between strong and weak transmissions.

Components List

D1, D2	1N914, or 1N4148 high speed silicon diodes
R1	2.2MΩ ¼W
C1, C2	0.1µF capacitor
C3	0.047µF capacitor

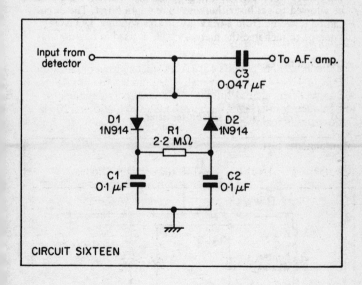

CIRCUIT SIXTEEN

CIRCUIT SEVENTEEN

DRY BATTERY RECHARGER
FOR LECLANCHÉ TYPE CELLS

This is a simple recharger or to be more accurate re-energiser for partially exhausted dry batteries, the circuit can recharge three 1½V batteries or one 4½V type at a time.

The 270Ω across the 1N4001 rectifier passes a small AC current through the battery and improves the process.

The batteries should only be partially exhausted before attempting a recharge, any completely exhausted batteries or ones which are leaking are useless and should be discarded. During the process the batteries will get warm but batteries should not be allowed to get hot otherwise they might burst. The circuit can be powered from a 6.3V AC heater winding. DO NOT attempt to recharge the mercury cells as used in hearing aids.

Components List

R1	22Ω 5W wire wound
R2	270Ω ½W
D1	1N4001 silicon rectifier

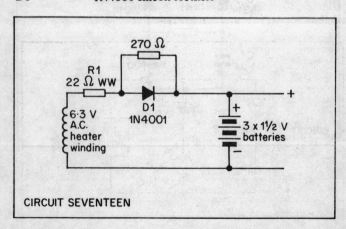

CIRCUIT SEVENTEEN

CIRCUIT EIGHTEEN

PORTABLE 12 VOLT TELEVISION
REVERSE POLARITY PROTECTION DEVICE

This is a protection device for a small screen portable mains/
battery television. Such portable TVs are now very common
and are designed to work either from mains or a 12 volt car
battery. Unfortunately a common fault is damage caused by
connecting the car battery the wrong way round i.e. polarity
reversed. The rectifier D2 will only conduct when the battery
is correctly connected, the rectifier specified is a 3 amp type
and the circuit is suitable for any portable 12V television.
If the car battery is connected with reverse polarity D2 will
not conduct protecting the TV circuit, however D1 is now
forward biased and will conduct passing current through the
12V indicator bulb. The 12V bulb glows to indicate
"FAULT" — BATTERY reversed.

Components List

D2	1N5400 3A rectifier diode
D1	1N4001 rectifier
Bulb	12V low current type

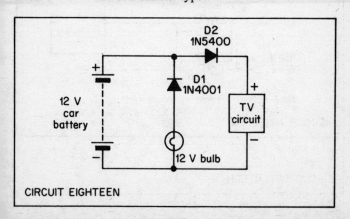

CIRCUIT EIGHTEEN

CIRCUIT NINETEEN

SOLDERING IRON SIMMER CONTROL

This is a very simple circuit to enable a soldering iron to run at reduced power in pauses between soldering, ideal when a soldering iron is in intermittent use over a long period. The lower temperature helps to prevent deterioration of the bit when not in actual use, when the iron is required for soldering it can be switched to full power and will heat up rapidly.

When the switch is in the OFF position the soldering iron is fed via the 1N4007 rectifier with current, the power produced in the iron is 0.707 (NOT HALF!) of normal. With the switch in the ON position the rectifier is shorted out and the iron receives full power. The circuit is at mains potential and must be enclosed to prevent risk of shock, the SPST switch must be rated for mains use, many small switches are only rated for 100 volt use. The rectifier must be a 1N4007 1000 piv type for 240V mains use.

The circuit could also be used as a simple lamp dimmer with a low wattage mains bulb, e.g. a 60W bulb used with the circuit can be switched to either bright or dimmed.

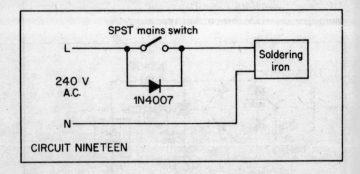

CIRCUIT TWENTY

IMPROVING THE POWER SUPPLY
IN MAINS/BATTERY TRANSISTOR RADIOS

With the increasing cost of dry batteries many transistor radios
are now on sale which are for mains/battery operation, they
incorporate a miniature mains transformer and power supply.
Many of these mains/battery radios use half wave rectification
and as a result hum is noticeable when the volume is low. A
simple way to improve hum performance is to convert the
circuit to full wave bridge rectification. The easiest way is to
remove the original rectifier and replace it with four miniature
1N4001 silicon rectifiers as in circuit (b).

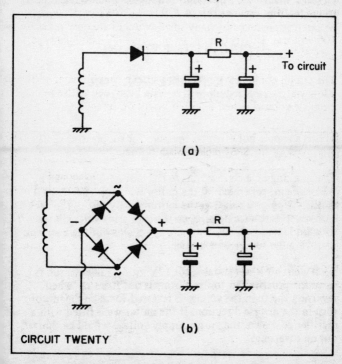

CIRCUIT TWENTY

29

Note that in the circuit before modification, diagram 20(a), one side of the transformer is connected to chassis for the conversion this connection is removed and both of the transformer secondary connections are made to the bridge rectifier.

With the half wave circuit the ripple frequency is 50Hz with the bridge circuit the ripple frequency is doubled to 100Hz this in effect doubles the smoothing action of the smoothing capacitors

$$\text{since } X_c = \frac{1}{2\pi FC}$$

The ease with which capacitors can shunt AC to chassis increases with increase in frequency i.e. hum is reduced. The circuits illustrated are negative earth the same dodge can be used with positive earth supplies by reversing polarities.

On 60Hz mains, the ripple frequency would be 60 Hz, the bridge rectifier doubles this to 120 Hz.

CIRCUIT TWENTY-ONE

SPARK SUPPRESSOR FOR LOW VOLTAGE DC MOTORS

This is a simple but effective measure for suppressing sparks produced by small low voltage DC motors.

The sparking of such low voltage DC motors is produced by the back emf generated by the motor winding. The 1N4001 rectifier is reverse biased to the motor supply but to the back emf which is reverse polarity to the energising voltage it is forward biased hence it conducts and shorts out the back emf removing the source of sparking.

Such a circuit is not suitable for 12V model railway motors since the polarity fed to the motors is not fixed i.e. when reversing the train the voltage is reversed to make the motor turn in the reverse direction. If the motor were fitted with a rectifier as shown, the motor supply voltage would be shorted out on reversing.

30

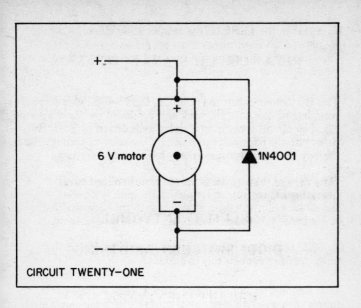

CIRCUIT TWENTY-ONE

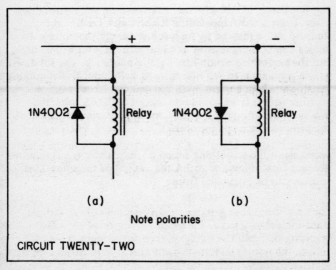

Note polarities

CIRCUIT TWENTY-TWO

CIRCUIT TWENTY-TWO

RELAY CIRCUIT SPARK SUPPRESSOR

This is a similar circuit to circuit 21, the 1N4002 silicon rectifier conducts to short out the back emf produced by the relay winding. This circuit is essential if the relay is driven by a transistor, otherwise the back emf produced by the relay operating might destroy the transistor since the voltage can be very high.

Note (a) and (b) rectifier is always reverse biased to relay operating supply.

CIRCUIT TWENTY-THREE

DIODE SWITCHED SMOOTHING

This is an add on smoothing circuit for a low voltage power supply. For a low voltage power supply with a high hum level the solution is to add a further resistance capacity smoothing stage. Hum is most apparent at low volume, i.e. low current demand and is masked by high volume levels, the voltage drop across a smoothing resistor at a high current level will be high, but the smoothing action is not really necessary. The solution to the problem is to use a rectifier to switch out the smoothing resistor at a high current level. The voltage across a silicon rectifier before it will conduct is about 0.7/0.75 volts, the values of the smoothing resistor and supply current are calculated to produce a voltage of 0.7V.

Example, if the smoothing action of the resistor is not required above a current level of 25mA the value of the smoothing resistor can be calculated from

$$V = IR$$
$$0.7 = V, \quad I = 0.025$$
$$0.025R = 0.7$$
$$R = \frac{0.7}{0.025}$$
$$R = 28\,\Omega$$

nearest value $27\,\Omega$

If resistor value is 27Ω maximum voltage drop across it is 0.7V, if a higher voltage drop is tolerable two silicon rectifiers can be connected in series to give a voltage drop of 1.4/1.5 volts and the value of the smoothing resistor can be doubled to 56 Ω. The circuit can be used with any value of current if the resistor is of suitable resistance and wattage rating, the rectifier used must be capable of passing the required current. The electrolytic capacitors must be of suitable value and voltage rating for the supply.

The circuit can be used with a negative earth supply (a) or positive earth supply (b) by reversing polarities.

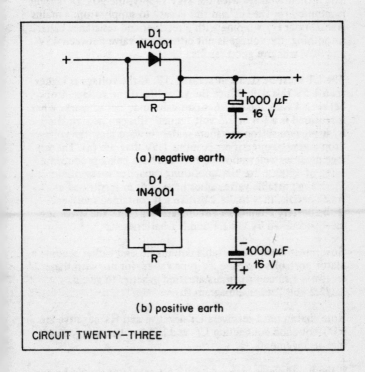

(a) negative earth

(b) positive earth

CIRCUIT TWENTY—THREE

CIRCUIT TWENTY-FOUR

CONVERTING BATTERY VALVE RECEIVERS TO MAINS OPERATION

There are many old battery valve receivers which are defunct due to batteries being unobtainable, these are capable of giving good service if converted to mains operation.

The difficulty arises with the 1½V supply, the 90V DC supply is required for the HT and this is easy to supply from a mains transformer HT winding with a rectifier and resistance capacity smoothing, the voltage is not critical any valve between 45V and 90V will give good results.

The LT must be stable at about 1.5V. If the voltage is higher than 1.5V this will reduce the valve life, if the voltage drops below 1.4 volts the DK96 mixer valve may fail to work. What is required is a 1.4 or 1.5 volt "zener" this can be simulated by using two silicon rectifiers under forward bias, the voltage drop across two rectifiers is about 1.5V diagram (a). The voltage must be well smoothed to avoid hum being produced a value of 4700μF for the smoothing capacitor is essential. Since the portable valve radios have built in ferrite rod or frame aerials, they make sensitive self contained receivers if the battery eliminator circuits are built into the space formerly occupied by the LT and HT batteries.

Government surplus portable equipment and earlier accumulator portables may use 2V type valves, for use with these receivers 3 silicon rectifiers are used in series to give a 2.1/2.2 volt "zener", diagram (b).

Note that in most receivers LT negative and HT negative are NOT common connecting LT- and HT- to chassis may upset bias arrangements.

If the hum level is high a 4700μF 6V capacitor should be connected across the 1N4001 rectifier as shown.

The value of the resistor R will depend on the valves used.

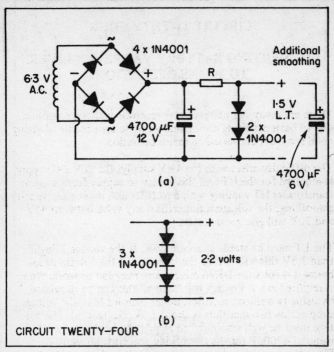

CIRCUIT TWENTY—FOUR

CIRCUIT TWENTY-FIVE

MAINS NEON FLASHER

This is a simple circuit for a mains powered neon flasher. The capacitor charges up via the 1N4007 rectifier until the voltage is equal to the firing voltage of the neon, the neon flashes partially discharging the capacitor, the capacitor charges up again until the neon flashes once more, the end result is that the neon flashes at a slow rate. The flash rate can be speeded up by using a lower value of capacitor, 0.47μF or 0.22μF 500V. With a value of 0.22μF 500V capacitor the circuit makes a useful flashing "ON" indicator for equipment. Note the circuit is at mains potential and must be used with care, it must be mounted so that no part of the circuit can be touched in use.

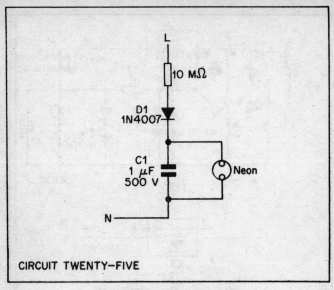

CIRCUIT TWENTY-SIX

USING ZENER/VOLTAGE
REGULATOR COMBINATIONS

Three terminal integrated circuit voltage regulators are now readily available in a standard range of voltages 5V, 12V, 15V, 18V and 24V. These units provide a simple, reliable means of voltage regulation — but what if one requires a non-standard voltage e.g. 27 volts?

The solution is to float the regulator above earth potential by connecting a zener diode of suitable wattage rating in series with the regulator earth lead. in circuit 26 a 3-volt zener is used, the voltage across the 24 volt regulator remains at 24 volts but the voltage as seen by the output is the regulator voltage plus the zener diode voltage 24 + 3 volts = 27 volts.

The usefulness of the circuit can be extended by switching out the zener as in 26(b) giving the regulator voltage as 24V or 27V or as in 26(c) by switching in another zener e.g. 6.2V rating giving voltages of 24V, 27V or 30V.

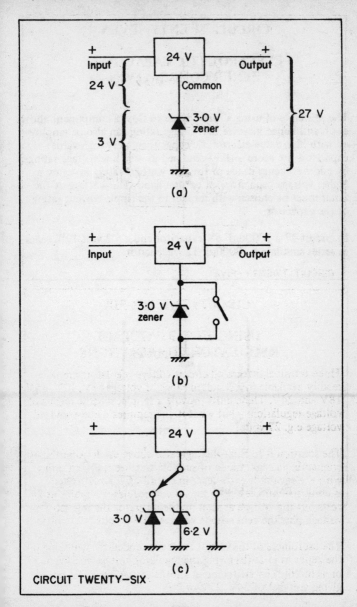

(a)

(b)

(c)

CIRCUIT TWENTY–SIX

CIRCUIT TWENTY-SEVEN

ELECTROLYTIC CAPACITOR/ ZENER COMBINATION

The principle of using a zener diode to float a component above earth and hence increase the voltage rating can also be employed with high value electrolytic capacitors. Very high value capacitors are more readily obtained in very low voltage ratings, by adding a zener diode of suitable wattage rating in series, a higher voltage capacitor can be simulated. The wattage of the zener must be chosen with respect to the ripple current rating of the capacitor.

In circuit 27 a 10000μF 6V capacitor and a 6.2 volt 10W zener in series simulate a 10000μF 12V capacitor.

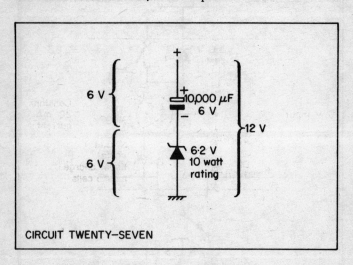

CIRCUIT TWENTY—SEVEN

CIRCUIT TWENTY-EIGHT

NICKEL-CADMIUM BATTERY CHARGER

This is a simple circuit for recharging small nickel cadmium (Nicad) batteries as used in pocket calculators. The circuit provides a constant charging current of 20mA for recharging 1 to 3 cells in series. The constant voltage drop across 2 silicon rectifiers under forward bias provides a reference for the 2N697 transistor, together they constitute a constant current supply of about 20mA. The circuit requires a 9V input, this could be obtained from a mains powered battery eliminator as used with transistor radios etc.

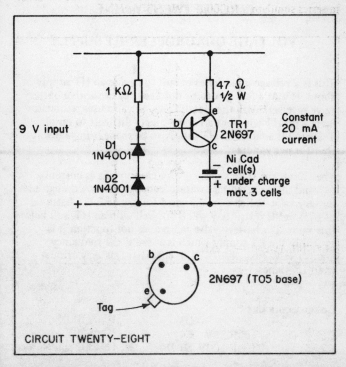

CIRCUIT TWENTY-EIGHT

Resistor R2 controls the value of the current supplied, the circuit can be adapted for higher currents by using a smaller value for R2 but if this is required a larger transistor such as a 2N3055 will be required. The transistor will get warm in operation and should be fitted with a TO5 heat sink, this is a simple clip-on device. The recharging current should be $\frac{1}{10}$ of the ampere hour capacity e.g. 50mA for a 500mA/hour cell.

Components List

R1	1K Ω
R2	47Ω ½W
D1	} 1N4001 silicon rectifier
D2	
TR1	2N697 transistor
TO5	heat sink

CIRCUIT TWENTY-NINE

VOLTAGE QUADRUPLER HT SUPPLY

This is a voltage quadrupler circuit to enable an HT supply of about 45V at a few mA to be obtained for use with a battery valve receiver. With the great decline in valve useage transformers with HT windings are increasingly difficult to obtain. This circuit enables an HT supply to be made using a 6 volt transformer winding.

The circuit can only supply a very low current as current demand increases voltage output drops rapidly. Although most battery valve radios were designed for use with HT batteries of 67½ or 90 volts, they will work well with an HT well below this value. If a battery valve radio does not function it is probably the LT supply which is at fault, the frequency changer valve (usually DK96 or equivalent) is very critical as to LT values.

Components List

		C3	10μF 100V
C1	10μF 25V	C4	10μF 50V
C2	10μF 100V	D1-D4	1N4002 silicon rec.

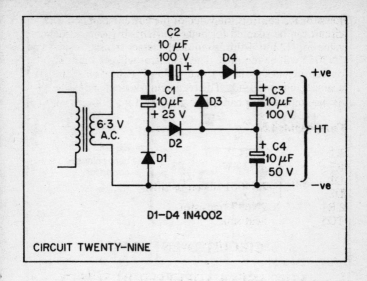

CIRCUIT TWENTY-NINE

CIRCUIT THIRTY

NON POLARISED HIGH VALUE CAPACITOR

There are circuits which require a very high value non polarised capacitor. A paper capacitor of value higher than about $2.2\mu F$ becomes very expensive. A non polarised capacitor can be simulated by connecting two electrolytics "back to back" i.e. in inverse series but the effective capacitor value is halved e.g. if two $10\mu F$ capacitors are connected in series the effective capacitance = $5\mu F$

$$\text{since} \quad \frac{1}{Ct} = \frac{1}{C1} + \frac{1}{C2}.$$

However by utilising two diodes and two identical electrolytic capacitors as in circuit 30, the effective value is equal to the value of the individual capacitor used. The rectifier diodes switch C1 and C2 in and out of circuit as the polarity applied to the circuit changes, so that the capacitor in circuit is polarised correctly for the voltage applied at that instant.

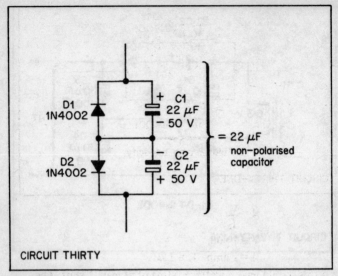

CIRCUIT THIRTY

Components List

D1, D2   1N4002
C1, C2   22μF 50V

The circuit can be used for higher voltages by using electrolytic capacitors of higher voltage ratings and rectifier diodes with a higher piv e.g. 1N4004.

CIRCUIT THIRTY-ONE

CONNECTING RECTIFIERS IN PARALLEL

If it is required to simulate a high current rectifier by connecting two rectifiers in parallel a low value resistor must be connected in series with each rectifier. The resistor compensates for differing forward characteristics of even supposedly identical rectifiers and ensures that the circuit current is divided equally between the two.

The resistor must produce a 1 volt drop at the rectifier current in the circuit shown (31) this is 1 AMP

42

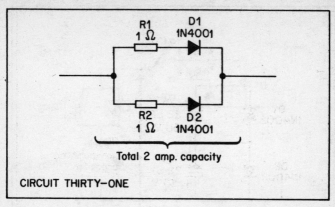

CIRCUIT THIRTY—ONE

Total 2 amp. capacity

$$R = \frac{V}{I}$$

$V = 1$ volt

$I = 1$ amp $R = 1\Omega$

and this should have a wattage rating of at least 1 watt. The rectifiers can now carry a maximum total current of 2 amps. For higher powers the equalising resistors will dissipate a lot of heat and should be mounted as far away from the rectifiers as possible.

Components List

D1, D2   2 x 1N4001
R1, R2   1Ω 1 watt wire wound

CIRCUIT THIRTY-TWO

DUAL RELAY CONTROL

This circuit uses four rectifiers to control two relays and a function switch connected by two wires only. The secret is the use of AC and switching rectifiers to feed the relays with DC of alternative polarity, the relays respond only to DC of their own appropriate polarity.

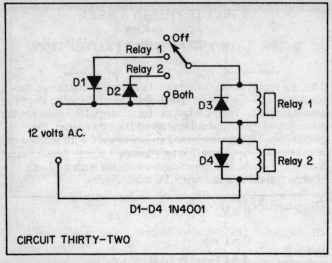

CIRCUIT THIRTY-TWO

This could be done by switching a battery supply but the use of AC means that a third function is possible if AC is fed to the relays both energise.

Components List

D1, D2, D3, D4	1N4001
Switch	1 pole 4 way switch
Relay 1, Relay 2	6V Relays

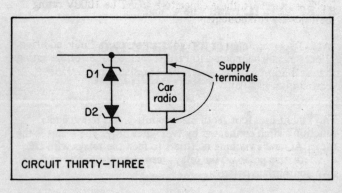

CIRCUIT THIRTY-THREE

44

CIRCUIT THIRTY-THREE

CAR RADIO TRANSIENT PROTECTION

This is a simple circuit using two 18V zener diodes to protect a car radio from the voltage transients generated by the electrical circuits in a car. The two diodes clip at about 18.7 volts i.e. the zener voltage plus forward voltage of the other zener, the circuit clips either polarity and so can be used with positive or negative earth equipment. Simply connect across the car radio supply terminals. 18V zener diodes are used with a 12-volt system. for a 6-volt use two 9.1V zener diodes.

Components List

D1, D2   18V 1W zener diodes

CIRCUIT THIRTY-FOUR

HIGHER VOLTAGE RECTIFIER

Circuit 34 illustrates the method used for connecting rectifiers in series to obtain a higher total voltage rating. The 470K Ω resistors compensate for varying characteristics of rectifiers and ensure that the applied voltage divides equally between the two rectifiers. The 0.01μF capacitors are to bypass voltage transients, these capacitors *MUST* be 1000V rating best quality components.

ALLOW a maximum of 250 volts across each diode, additional diodes can be connected to further increase the voltage rating but each must have its own 470KΩ resistor and 0.01μF capacitor in parallel.

Components List

Rectifier   1N4007 type
R1, R2   470K Ω½W
C1, C2   0.01μF 1000V rating

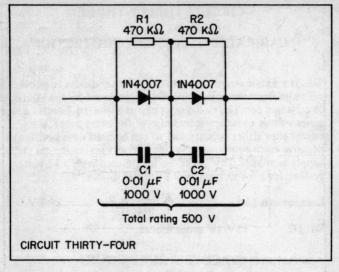

R1
470 KΩ

R2
470 KΩ

1N4007

1N4007

C1
0·01 μF
1000 V

C2
0·01 μF
1000 V

Total rating 500 V

CIRCUIT THIRTY—FOUR

CIRCUIT THIRTY-FIVE

DIODE DROPPER PROTECTION CIRCUIT

In television and radio circuits where a series connected valve heater chain is used an excellent alternative to a voltage dropping resistor is a diode dropper, the heater current passes through a rectifier which reduces the heater chain power to 0.707 of normal. This circuit has the great advantage that a rectifier diode dissipates very little heat as opposed to a heater dropper resistor. The reduction in heat dissipated inside the cabinet improves circuit reliability.
The great disadvantage of the diode dropper [circuit 35(a)] is that if the diode fails it goes short circuit and the full AC power passes through the heater chain over-running the valves.

The simple protection circuit removes this disadvantage. A second rectifier is connected across the heater chain, if Rectifier 1, the diode dropper, is functioning normally Rectifier 2 is reverse biased and passes no current, If Rectifier 1 fails and goes short circuit, Rectifier 2 is fed with AC and conducts, this represents a virtual short circuit across the heater line, a very heavy current flows and the fuse blows.

46

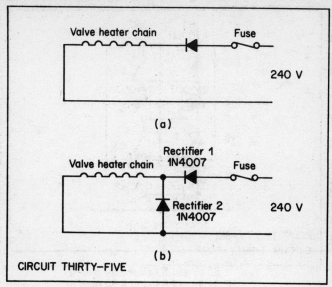

(a)

(b)

CIRCUIT THIRTY—FIVE

Components List

Rectifier 1, 2 1N4007
Fuse 250mA
  for 150mA heater chain
  500mA fuses, anti-surge type for 300mA heater chain

CIRCUIT THIRTY-SIX

THE SUPER ZENER

This is a circuit based on the use of the binary system to enable a whole series of stabilised voltages or reference voltages to be used in a power supply. The circuit simulates a multi-value zener, by connecting zeners in series.

If four zener diodes are used 3.0V, 6.2V, 12V, 24V which closely matches the binary type series 3, 6, 12, 24 by connecting in (switch open), or shorting out (switch closed), the diodes the circuit will stabilise the voltages 3, 6, 9, 12, 15, 18, 21, 24, 27, 30, 33, 36, 39, 42, 45. or in terms of the zeners used

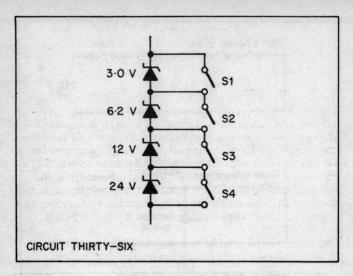

CIRCUIT THIRTY—SIX

3V	S2 closed S3 closed S4 closed
6V	S1 closed S3 closed S4 closed
9V = 3 + 6	S3 closed S4 closed
12V	S1 closed S2 closed S4 closed
15V = 3 + 12	S2 closed S4 closed
18V = 6 + 12	S1 closed S4 closed
21V = 3 + 6 + 12	S4 closed
24V	S1 closed S2 closed S3 closed
27V = 3 + 24	S2 closed S3 closed
30V = 6 + 24	S1 closed S3 closed
33V = 3 + 6 + 24	S3 closed
36V = 12 + 24	S1 closed S2 closed
39V = 3 + 12 + 24	S2 closed
42V = 6 + 12 + 24	S1 closed
45V = 3 + 6 + 12 + 24	All switches open

Components List

1	3.0V zener diode
1	6.2V zener diode
1	12V zener diode
1	24V zener diode
4	SPST switches

CIRCUIT THIRTY-SEVEN

ZENER VOLTAGE DROPPER

The zener is a voltage reference diode but it can be used as a voltage dropper as opposed to a resistor. The voltage drop across a zener is constant at the zener voltage. In circuit (37) the two zeners are used as an example, the zener Z1 stabilises the voltage at 9.1V with the switch in the OFF position the current flows through Z2 and there is a voltage drop of 3V, the output is 9-3V = 6V with Z2 shorted out, switch in the ON position, the output is 9 volts. The only consideration is the amount of power that must be dissipated by the zener i.e. it must be of a suitable wattage rating.

The zener has the great advantage over a dropper resistor, that the voltage drop is virtually independent of current.

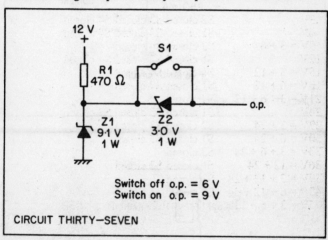

Switch off o.p. = 6 V
Switch on o.p. = 9 V

CIRCUIT THIRTY—SEVEN

Components List

S1	SPST switch
Z1	9.1V 1W
Z2	3.0V 1W
R1	470 Ω 1W

CIRCUIT THIRTY-EIGHT

ZENER PROTECTION FOR OVER-VOLTAGE

This is a very simple over-voltage protection circuit for 12 volt equipment which might be damaged by a voltage of over 15 volts. This could occur with equipment run from a car battery. If the voltage rises to 15 volts the zener diode conducts heavily and blows the fuse, thus disconnecting the supply. The zener specified is a 10-watt type for a 250mA fuse since 250mA is the continuous current the fuse will pass the current has to exceed this value before the fuse will blow and the zener diode must be rated to passing a fusing current of 500 mA. Fusing current is twice nominal fuse rating.

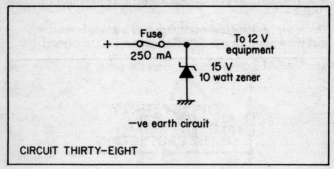

CIRCUIT THIRTY-EIGHT

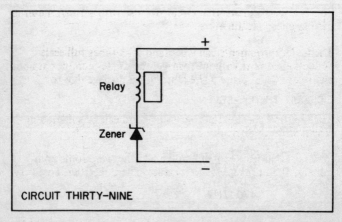

CIRCUIT THIRTY-NINE

CIRCUIT THIRTY-NINE

IMPROVING RELAY PERFORMANCE

Circuit 39 illustrates the use of zener diodes to improve the
ON/OFF ratio of operating voltages for a relay by connecting
a zener in series with the relay.

Example
Suppose that a relay is ON at 12 volts and off at 3 volts
the ON/OFF ratio is 4 : 1.

If a 7.5V zener is connected in series the ratio is on 12 + 7.5,
OFF 3 + 7.5

ratio 19.5 : 10.5
or almost 2 : 1.

The ON/OFF current ratio remains the same.

CIRCUIT FORTY

METER PROTECTION

This is a simple protection circuit for use with a 1 mA meter as
used in cheap multimeters.

The meter movements can withstand 2—3 times full scale
deflection current without damage, the diodes conduct at about
about 2 mA and protect the meter from damage due to
overload.

The rectifiers specified are very small and can be soldered in
circuit without difficulty.

Meters are quite expensive, unlike all other electronic components their price tends to increase. The 2 rectifiers cost very
little.

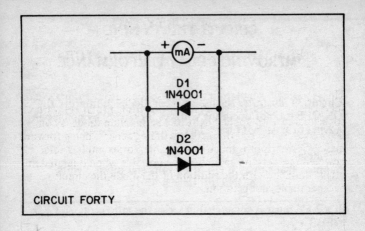

CIRCUIT FORTY

CIRCUIT FORTY-ONE

SUPPRESSED ZERO VOLTMETER

For some applications a suppressed zero voltmeter is more useful than a conventional one e.g. for checking a 12 volt car battery the voltages of interest are between 10 and 15, the voltages of a discharged and fully charged battery. If a zener diode is connected in series with a voltmeter, the zener diode will not conduct until the voltage being measured exceeds the zener voltage. For circuit (41) a 10V 400mW zener diode is connected in series with a 5V voltmeter, the voltmeter scale should be calibrated 10 to 15V instead of 0 to 5 volts.

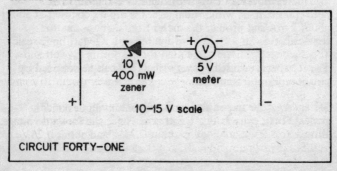

CIRCUIT FORTY-ONE

CIRCUIT FORTY-TWO

SILICON SOLAR CELL REGULATOR

This is a simple adaptation to stabilise the output from a silicon solar cell or "sun battery". The output from a solar cell varies considerably with applied light. If a germanium diode is connected across the cell this acts as a 0.2V "zener", being forward biased. The output is much more stable, for example a solar powered regenerative radio became unstable when operated in bright sunlight, with the addition of the diode the circuit became stable, in operation.

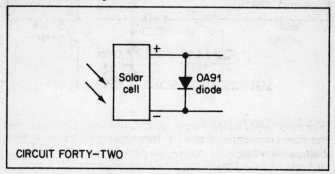

CIRCUIT FORTY—TWO

CIRCUIT FORTY-THREE

LOGARITHMIC SCALE VOLTMETER

This circuit is for a 0—10V voltmeter with a logarithmic scale this enables the meter to be used for measuring 1½ volt and 9 volt batteries with the same scale. The scale is extended up to about 2V and is increasingly compressed up to the 10V end.

D1 and D2, the two silicon and germanium diodes under forward bias, constitute a 1 volt zener since the forward voltage drop across a silicon diode is about 0.75V, and about 0.25V across a germanium diode, 0.75 + 0.25 = 1 volt.

The 1 volt bias prevents D3 from conducting until the input voltage is over 1 volt so that the scale up to the 1V point is linear. At voltages over 1 volt D3 conducts bypassing current from the meter so that the scale becomes increasingly non linear and compressed, the result is that the meter approximates to a logarithmic scale. The meter for the voltmeter should be a 50 microamp type, the scale will require calibration against standard voltages up to 10V.

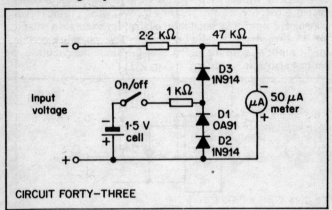

CIRCUIT FORTY—THREE

Components List

R1	2.2K Ω 5% ¼W
R2	47K Ω 5% ¼W
R3	1K Ω
D1	OA91
D2, D3	1N914 or 1N4148
Switch	SPST
Meter	50µA type

CIRCUIT FORTY-FOUR

GRID-BIAS SUPPLY

This is a circuit to supply negative bias voltage from a 6.3V AC heater winding. This may be of interest to vintage radio enthusiasts who are considering converting an ancient battery type radio to mains use. Many old type "wirelesses" used HT,

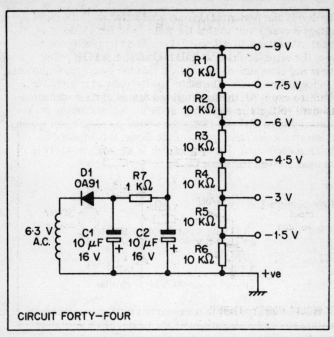

CIRCUIT FORTY—FOUR

accumulator for LT and GB (grid-bias) batteries. The circuit gives a tapped GB supply, of 1½, 3, 4½, 6, 7½ and 9V.

A germanium diode type OA91 is used as the rectifier because of the tiny current required.

Components List

R1-R6	10KΩ ¼W
D1	OA91 germanium diode
C1, C2	10µF 16V
R7	1KΩ ¼W

CIRCUIT FORTY-FIVE

TUNNEL DIODE OSCILLATOR

This is a novel AF oscillator using a tunnel diode as the active
device. VR1, R1 and R2 form a low impedance supply for the
tunnel diode. VR1 is a 1K Ω wire wound potentiometer which
controls the operating point of the diode, it is adjusted for
loudest oscillation. The loudspeaker is a miniature 8 Ω type
as used in small transistor radios.

Components List

VR1   1K Ω wire wound potentiometer
R1   47 1W
R2   10 Ω 1W
C1   0.47μF
Diode   Tunnel diode AEY11 or similar

It must be emphasised that this circuit is of an experimental
nature and some adjustment of the tunnel diode operating
conditions may be necessary for successful operation.

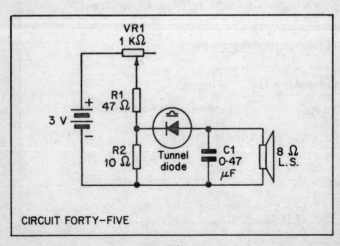

CIRCUIT FORTY-FIVE

CIRCUIT FORTY-SIX

USING ZENER DIODES

A zener diode provides a simple means of regulating voltage
supplies. In circuit 46 (a) and (b) a stabilised 9V supply is
derived from a 12V input. The resistor R1 limits the maximum
current that can flow through Z1. A zener diode can stabilise
a positive supply 46(a) or a negative supply 46(b). The zener
diode must have a suitable wattage rating for the current which
flows through the circuit WITH NO LOAD CONNECTED.

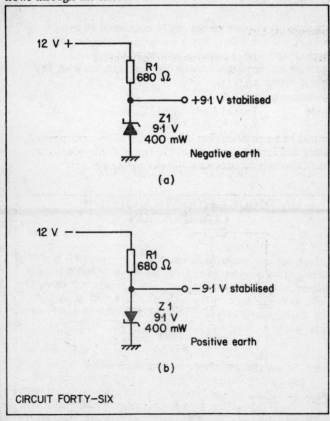

CIRCUIT FORTY—SIX

Zener wattage = zener voltage X current
for a 400mW diode

$$\text{maximum current} = \frac{\text{wattage}}{\text{zener voltage}}$$

If wattage is in mW
current is in mA

$$\text{maximum current} = \frac{400}{9.1} \text{ mA}$$

$$" \qquad = 44\text{mA}$$

To allow for a margin of safety the maximum current should
be limited to 40mA.

Remember that zener diodes can be connected in series.
An 18 volt 400mW can carry a maximum current of about
20mA. If two 9.1V zeners are connected in series each 9.1
zener can handle 40mA, so together they constitute an 18V
800mW zener.

Components List

Z1	9.1V 400mW zener
R1	680Ω ½W

CIRCUIT FORTY-SEVEN

DIODE/ZENER/TRANSISTOR COMBINATION

If a high current regulated power supply is required it is possible
to use a heavy duty zener of 10 or 20 W rating, but it is more
economical to use a zener diode to bias a power transistor. The
power transistor handles the current up to several amps, the
zener diode merely provides a reference for the transistor as in
circuit 47(a).

One disadvantage of this circuit is that there is a voltage drop
across the transistor so that there is a difference between the
zener voltage and the output voltage, a simple correcting
measure is to connect a silicon rectifier in series with the zener
diode so that the voltage drop across the power transistor is

compensated for by a similar increase in the voltage between the transistor base and chassis due to the forward voltage drop across the rectifier, circuit 47(b). Alternatively a zener of slightly higher voltage than the required output voltage is used, e.g. for a 6V supply instead of a 6.2V zener use a 6.8 volt zener.

Components List

		D1	1N4001 rectifier
		TR1	2N3055 transistor
R1	680 Ω ½W	C1	10µF 16V electrolytic
Z1	9.1V 400mW zener		

(a)

(b)

CIRCUIT FORTY-SEVEN

CIRCUIT FORTY-EIGHT

CONNECTING BATTERIES IN PARALLEL

If batteries are connected in parallel one may discharge through
the other due to a difference in the internal resistance of even
apparently identical batteries. However, if a silicon rectifier is
connected in series with each battery this prevents mutual discharge since the current can now only flow one way, through
the load.

The rectifiers used must be capable of passing the required
battery current. If a current higher than 1 amp is required,
heavy duty 3A, 10 or 35 amp rectifiers should be used.
Although two batteries are shown in the diagram, any number
can be connected in parallel if each one is fitted with a rectifier.

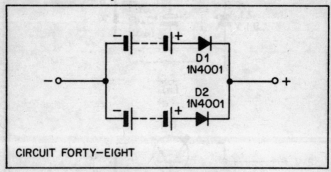

CIRCUIT FORTY-EIGHT

CIRCUIT FORTY-NINE

AUTOMATIC BATTERY/MAINS SWITCHING

This is a simple diode circuit to give automatic switching from
battery supply to a mains derived power supply.

The essential requirement for a reliable switching action is that
on "MAINS" the supply is slightly higher, about 1 VOLT
higher is suggested, than the new battery voltage. If the supply,
when operating from the mains, is zener stabilised this ensures

60

reliable circuit action. In diagram 49(a) with mains operation the voltage at the cathode D2 is +6.8V, the voltage at the anode is 6V (or less with used battery) so that the anode is less positive than the cathode, i.e. the anode IS NEGATIVE WITH RESPECT TO THE CATHODE, this means that the diode is reverse biased and will not conduct, hence no current

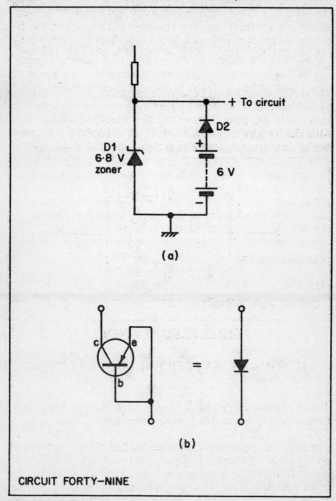

(a)

(b)

CIRCUIT FORTY—NINE

flows from the battery. If the mains supply is removed the diode D2 conducts and the circuit runs from the battery. For minimum voltage drop across the diode a germanium rectifier should be used. If a germanium type rectifier is not available an OUTPUT type germanium transistor can be used. The base and emitter are connected together, this corresponds to the cathode of a rectifier, the collector corresponds to the anode.

A silicon type rectifier can be used if the higher voltage drop across it can be tolerated. The rectifier used must be capable of passing the current required by the circuit if this is very low, 5mA or less, an OA91 germanium diode could be used.

CIRCUIT FIFTY

BRIDGE RECTIFIER POLARITY PROTECTION

With an electronic circuit which is designed to operate from a 12 volt battery e.g. car equipment, portable TV, there is always the risk that the battery could be connected the wrong way round with subsequent damage. If the circuit is connected to the battery via a bridge rectifier the bridge rectifier automatically switches the battery to the correct polarity to operate the circuit, thus making battery connection 'fool proof'. The bridge in circuit 50 is suitable for currents up to 3 amps.

Components List

D1—D4   1N5400 silicon rectifiers

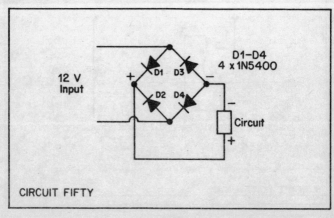

CIRCUIT FIFTY

Please note overleaf is a list of other titles that are available in our range of Radio and Electronic Books.

These should be available from most good Booksellers, Radio Component Dealers and Mail Order Companies.

However, should you experience difficulty in obtaining any title in your area, then please write directly to the publishers enclosing payment to cover the cost of the book plus adequate postage.

BERNARD BABANI (publishing) LTD
THE GRAMPIANS
SHEPHERDS BUSH ROAD
LONDON W6 7NF
ENGLAND